everything beautiful

TO THE PARENTS

Young children may have joyous experiences of companionship with God if they are not hurried. "Saying prayers" is not likely to be the first step. Delighting in the sights and sounds and "feels" in the world about them, children may come to associate the creation with God, the Creator, through simple interpretation. "God planned it for us."

Experiencing love and care in their families, they may come to associate love and care with God through simple interpretations. "Mother loves you. God loves you much more."

The small child's first response to God is likely to be through acts rather than through words. He says "Thank you" for God's creation when, happily, he runs in the sunshine or drinks the good milk or imitates the flying bird.

But, as he grows, he needs to pin down experiences with language. And so we suggest some prayers which parents may use with their children to help them think more clearly about God and his goodness and to express their response to his love.

It is hoped that the words of these prayers, as they are read to children, will help them to think their own thoughts and to say their own words as they come increasingly to wish to talk with God.

Mary Alice Jones

PRAYERS and GRACES
for a small child

By MARY ALICE JONES

in collaboration with KATE SMALLWOOD

Illustrated by Elizabeth Webbe

RAND McNALLY & COMPANY : Chicago

WHEN I WAKE UP

Out of my window
  My yard looks so gay!
I feel God is near me,
  And so I will pray.

MORNING SONG

Early in the morning
  I sing a happy song:
"God will be my helper,
  All this whole day long!"

THANK YOU

Thank you, dear God,
    For sleep through the night;
Thank you, dear God,
    For the glad morning light.

IN THE MORNING

In the morning, in the morning,
In the morning comes the sun!
In the morning, in the morning,
I am glad the day's begun!
In the morning, in the morning,
Pray, "God bless us, every one!"

GOD'S LOVE

Thank you, God, that I can feel
Your love about me all this day.

HELP ME TODAY

Dear God, please help me to say
Kind words to all my friends today;
Dear God, please help me to play
With all my friends in a happy way.

FOR EYES TO SEE

Thank you, God, for eyes to see
A river and a tree,
A baby kitten that's so wee,
And my mother's face as she looks at me.

GRACE

God is great
   And God is good;
Let us thank him
   For our food.

THANK YOU, GOD

Thank you, God,
For milk and, bread
And other things so good;
Thank you, God,
For those who help
To grow and cook our food.

Elizabeth McE. Shields

HAPPY THOUGHTS

I'm glad, I'm glad, I'm glad today!
I'm glad that I can run and play.
   I'm glad that I can see the sky,
   I'm glad that I can swing up high.
I'm glad, I'm glad, I'm glad today!
I'm glad, dear God! That's how I pray.

TO BE A HELPER

My mother and my daddy
   Work hard for me and are kind.
I want to help them, too, dear God,
   In every way I can find.

KIND PEOPLE

I thought about the carpenter
Who made our house snug and warm;

I thought about the farmer
Who grows our food on his farm;

I thought about kind people
Who work for us each day.

And then I thought of thanking God—
And that is how I pray.

FOR THE GOOD WORLD

Thank you, dear God,
For the good world you have planned:
For rain and wind and snowflakes;

For trees and grass and flowers;
For birds and pets and horses;

For books and music and pictures;
For home and school and church.
   Thank you, dear God,
For the good world you have planned.

FOR LOVING ME

Thank you, dear God, for loving me
When I do the things I should;
Thank you, God, for loving me
Even when I am not good.
Thank you, God, for loving me.

ON A STORMY NIGHT

The thunder is noisier than I like,
   And the lightning is very bright.
Help me, God, to feel you near
   On a windy and stormy night.

I THINK OF GOD AND MOTHER

I think God is like my mother:
    She helps me the whole day through,
And comforts me when I'm sorry,
    And loves me whatever I do.

I THINK OF GOD AND DADDY

I think God is like my daddy:
    I'm not afraid when he's near.
He knows how to answer my questions,
    And he's never too busy to hear.

A HAPPY DAY

It's been a happy day, dear God.
I helped my mother bake a cake
And played with Mary on the swing
And watched the ducks swim on the lake.
It's been a happy day, dear God.

GOOD NIGHT

Good night, good night, good night
To friendly helpers everywhere.
   God help you all,
   God bless you all,
And keep you in his loving care.

THANK GOD FOR NIGHT

Thank you, God, for the night—
    For the shining stars
    And the quiet dark,
    For my own little bed
    And for rest and sleep.
Thank you, God, for the night.

THANKS FOR CARE

I thank you for your care, dear God,
    Before I go to sleep,
And send my love all 'round my block
    To all the people in your keep.

OFF TO SLEEP

I've had my good-night kiss and hug,
And now I'm all tucked in and snug.
Good night, dear God,
I'm going to sleep.
I know that you are near.

God . . . has made